• HBJ READING PROGRAM •

MORTIMER FROG

LAUREATE EDITION

LEVEL 2

Bernice E. Cullinan
Roger C. Farr
W. Dorsey Hammond
Nancy L. Roser
Dorothy S. Strickland

Stories by Elizabeth K. Cooper

D1223099

HBJ **HARCOURT BRACE JOVANOVICH, PUBLISHERS**
Orlando   San Diego   Chicago   Dallas

Acknowledgments

Grateful acknowledgment is made to *Greenwillow Books, a division of William Morrow & Company, Inc.* for permission to reprint "Bullfrogs" from *Ride a Purple Pelican* by Jack Prelutsky. Text copyright © 1986 by Jack Prelutsky.

Illustrators

Dee Deloy: cover, Sally Schaedler: 4–51, Lynn Titleman: 52–53, Cynthia Ann Brodie: 54–63, Mary McLaren, 64–71

Printed in the United States of America

ISBN 0-15-330003-5

Contents

4

The Surprise

"Mrs. Lee, see what I have!" said Meg.

"What do you have, Meg?" asked Mrs. Lee.

"I have a surprise," said Meg.

"A surprise can be fun.
What is the surprise, Meg?"
asked Mrs. Lee.

"The surprise is Mortimer.
Mortimer is a frog!" said Meg.

"I like frogs," said Mrs. Lee.
"Mortimer is a good surprise."

6

"Mortimer can go in here.
The girls will like Mortimer.
The boys will, too," said Mrs. Lee.

"Here come the boys and girls
now," said Meg.

"Boys and girls, look at Mortimer.
Mortimer is a surprise from Meg.
Do you like the surprise?"
asked Mrs. Lee.

"Yes, we like the little frog,"
said the girls.

"I do not like frogs," said Sam.

"Will you be good to Mortimer?" asked Mrs. Lee.

"Yes, we will be good to the little frog," said the boys and girls.

Mortimer Hops!

"Sam, take a look at this.
See this big frog.
It looks like Mortimer,"
said Meg.

"I don't want to look at
that frog," said Sam.
"I don't like frogs."

"Come and see Mortimer take big hops," said Rita.

"I don't want to see Mortimer hop," said Sam.
"I don't like frogs."

"I like frogs," said Rita.
"I like Mortimer."

"I like big frogs and little frogs," said Todd.

"Look at Mortimer hop!"
said Rita.

"Mortimer likes to hop.
I think Mortimer likes it here,"
said Todd.

"I do, too," said Meg.

"Do you think Mortimer can get out?" asked Todd.

"I don't think Mortimer can get out," said Meg.
"Mortimer can't take a hop that big."

"Good!" said Sam.
"I don't want Mortimer to get out."

Mrs. Lee said, "Boys and girls, we have to go out to play now."

"Can we take Mortimer with us?" asked Meg.

"We can't do that," said Mrs. Lee. "Mortimer likes it in here."

"Good," said Sam. "I don't want Mortimer to go out with us."

Where Is Mortimer?

"Mrs. Lee, Mrs. Lee!" said Meg.
"I can't find Mortimer!
He is not here."

Rita asked, "Where is Mortimer?
Where did he go?"

"How did Mortimer get out?"
asked Todd.

"Did he hop out?"

"We have to find him,"
said Rita.

"Where will you look for Mortimer?" asked Mrs. Lee.

"I will look here," said Meg. "Todd, will you help me?"

"Yes, I will," said Todd.

"I will help you, too," said Rita.

Meg, Rita, and Todd looked for Mortimer.

They did not find him.

"We will look for Mortimer," said Mrs. Lee.

"I don't want to look," said Sam.

"You can help me look, Sam," said Mrs. Lee.

"We have to find Mortimer,"
said Meg.

"It is not good for him to be out."

"We will find him," said Mrs. Lee.

What do you think Mortimer
will do?

They Find Mortimer

"I see Mortimer!" said Sam.
"He is up there."

"I don't see Mortimer.
Where is he?" asked Meg.

"Look up there," said Sam.
"Mortimer is up there.
See him hop."

"There he is," said Rita.
"Now I see him."

"I see him, too," said Todd.

"Can he get down?" asked Meg.

"Mortimer can get down,"
said Mrs. Lee.

"He went up. He can get down."

The boys and girls looked
at Mortimer.

Mortimer looked at them.

Mortimer went
hop,
hop,
hop.

"Did you see Mortimer hop?"
asked Sam.

"Mortimer takes big hops."

"I will get Mortimer,"
said Meg.

"I will put him in the tank."

"Is this tank too little for
Mortimer now?" asked Todd.

"Yes, this tank is too little.
We have to get a new tank,"
said Sam.

"Mrs. Lee, do you have a
new tank for Mortimer?"
asked Rita.

"Yes," said Mrs. Lee.
"Here is a new tank.
It is a big tank."

"Will Mortimer hop out?"
asked Todd.

"This big tank will stop Mortimer,"
said Mrs. Lee.

Meg put Mortimer in the big tank.
The boys and girls looked
at Mortimer.

Mortimer looked at them.

Mortimer went hop, hop, hop in the
big tank.

"What makes Mortimer want
to hop?" asked Todd.

"I think Mortimer just likes
to hop," said Sam.

Mortimer Gets Out

"Oh, no!" said Meg.
"Mortimer isn't in his tank."

"Can you see him?" asked Rita.

"No, I can't," said Meg.
"We will have to look for him."

"Come here, Mortimer,"
said Todd.

"I don't want Mortimer
to be out of his tank,"
said Sam.

"Oh, here is Mortimer!" said Kim.
"Come out, Mortimer!
What are you doing in there?"

"Mortimer is just playing,"
said Sam.

"I will take him, Kim.
I will put him in his tank,"
said Meg.

"What are we going to do with you, Mortimer?

You can't hop in and out like this.

You will just have to stop it," said Meg.

"Mortimer can't stop it," said Todd.

"Mortimer is a big frog now. He takes big hops."

"Mortimer is too big for
his tank now," said Rita.
  "I don't think we can keep him."

  "I like Mortimer.
  I want to keep him,"
said Meg.

  "I want to keep him, too,"
said Rita.
  "Mortimer is just too big."

"Mortimer isn't too big," said Meg.

"His tank is too little."

"Can we get a big, big tank to put him in?" asked Kim.

"We will ask Mrs. Lee," said Sam.

Do you think they will get a big, big tank for Mortimer?

Where Will Mortimer Go?

"Mortimer is too big for his tank, Mrs. Lee," said Sam.

"He has to have a new tank."

"Can we get a big, big tank to put him in?" asked Meg.

"Do you think Mortimer wants a new tank?" asked Mrs. Lee.

"I think Mortimer likes to take big hops," said Todd.

"He can't take big hops in this tank. This tank isn't a good home for Mortimer now."

"He may want a new home," said Kim.

The boys and girls looked
at Mrs. Lee.
She looked at them.

"He may want a new home
at the pond," said Kim.

"I think that is just what
Mortimer wants," said Todd.

"I don't want Mortimer to go
to the pond," said Meg.

"I don't want to let him go.

I just want to keep him here."

Meg looked at Mortimer.

"May we keep him?

Do we have to let him go?"
asked Sam.

"I think Mortimer has to have a new home," said Mrs. Lee.

"The pond will be a good home for Mortimer."

"How can we get Mortimer to the pond?" asked Kim.

"My dad can take us," said Todd.
"He can take us in his van."

"We can help Mortimer find a
new home at the pond," said Kim.

Do you think Meg and Sam
will help Mortimer find a
new home?

A New Home
for Mortimer

"This is my dad," said Todd.
"He will take all of us to the
pond in his van."

"We are happy you will take us
to the pond," said Mrs. Lee.
"We want to help Mortimer find
a new home."

40

"Meg, get Mortimer out of the tank.
Put him in the box," said Mrs. Lee.

"Mortimer is in the box,"
said Meg.

"Now we can all go to the van,"
said Mrs. Lee.

"I don't think Mortimer will like the pond," said Meg.

"It may be too big for him."

"Meg, you want to keep him, don't you?" asked Mrs. Lee.

"I want to keep him, too," said Sam.

"Mortimer will like the pond,"
said Mrs. Lee.

"All frogs like ponds.
Big frogs and little frogs
will be there.

The pond will be a good
home for Mortimer."

"Boys and girls, you may all get
out of the van now," said Mrs. Lee.

"Meg, don't let Mortimer out
of the box.

We will take him out
at the pond."

Do you think Mortimer will like
his new home at the pond?

The Pond

"Look at all the frogs!"
said Meg.

"Mortimer will like them,"
said Mrs. Lee.
"Mortimer can play with them.
He will be happy here."

"May we let Mortimer go now?"
asked Rita.

"Not yet," said Meg.

"I want a picture of Mortimer."

"My dad can take the picture," said Todd.

"Meg, take Mortimer out of the box now," said Mrs. Lee.

"Let Sam help you."

"Let Mortimer go now.
Let him hop to the pond,"
said Mrs. Lee.

"What will Mortimer do for food?"
asked Meg.

"There is food in the pond,"
said Mrs. Lee.
"Mortimer will find it."

Mortimer went hop, hop, hop.

Sam looked in the pond.
He did not find Mortimer.

"Where is Mortimer?" asked Sam.
"I can't find him now."

"Is that Mortimer?" asked Rita.

"That can't be Mortimer.
That frog is too little,"
said Todd.

"Is that Mortimer?" asked Kim.

"No, that frog is too big,"
said Sam.

"All of the frogs look like
Mortimer," said Meg.
"What a surprise!"

"I think Mortimer likes his new home," said Sam.

"He can take big hops here."

"I think Mortimer will be happy here," said Meg.

"This is a good home for Mortimer."

Bullfrogs

by Jack Prelutsky

Bullfrogs, bullfrogs on parade,
dressed in gold and green brocade,
scarlet buttons on their suits,
fringes on their bumbershoots.

See them tip their satin hats
as they bounce like acrobats,
hear them croak a serenade,
bullfrogs, bullfrogs on parade.

53

The Picture

by Eve Bunting

Southern California Council
for Literature Award

"May I take a picture
of you, Pig?" Bear asked.

"Oh, yes," said Pig.
"I will like that."

54

"Bird, may I have some things for my picture?" asked Pig.

"What do you want?" asked Bird.

"I want some things to make me look good," Pig said.

"I will let you have some things to make you look good, Pig," said Bird.

"Now I look good," Pig said.
"Bear will like me with all the new things.
I will surprise Bear.
Bear will be happy."

"I don't see Pig,"
said Bear.
"Where is Pig?"

"This is Pig," said Bird.

"No, that isn't Pig,"
said Bear.

"Yes, I am Pig!"
said Pig.

"I wanted to look good
for the picture."

"You don't look like Pig now,"
Bear said.

58

"How do I look now?"
Pig asked.

"You look like Pig.
You look good.
Now I will take the picture,"
said Bear.

"May I take a picture
of you, Bear?" asked Pig.

"Yes, but I want to find Frog,"
said Bear.

"Frog, will that hat make me look good in the picture?" asked Bear.

"Yes, this hat will make you look good," said Frog.

"May I have the hat?" asked Bear.

"Yes, you may have the hat," said Frog.

"Bear, what do you have?"
asked Pig.

"I have a hat.
I want to look good in
the picture," said Bear.

"You don't have to have a hat
to look good," said Pig.

"We don't have to get new
things to make us look good,"
said Pig.

"No, we don't," said Bear.
"We look good just being us."

Word Helper

"Word Helper" develops readiness for dictionary skills and provides students with a reference for words they may wish to use in their writing. Example sentences for all new words in this book are provided. Illustrated sentences are followed by ■.

Aa

all I think **all** the boys are here. ■

am I **am** going to see Todd.

are We **are** going to surprise Meg.

ask I will **ask** Mrs. Lee.

asked The girls **asked** for a dog.

Bb

being Mortimer is **being** a good frog.

64

box   The surprise is in the
        box. ■

boys The **boys** will go in the
        boat.

but   I want to go, **but** I can't.

Cc

can't I can not help you.
        I **can't** help you.

Dd

dad   My **dad** is here now.

doing What is Mortimer **doing**?

don't I do not want to go.
        I **don't** want to go. ■

Ff

find   The girls will **find** the frog.

food   This **food** is for the dog. ■

frog   This **frog** is little.

Gg

girls   The **girls** like the little bear. ■

going   Where is Mrs. Lee **going**?

Hh

happy   The girl is **happy.** ■

has   Kim **has** a new dog.

hat   The **hat** has a funny flower.

he	Todd likes dogs. **He** wants this dog.
him	The boys will go with Sam. The boys will go with **him.**
his	Todd will take **his** frog now.
home	They will come **home.**
hop	Can you **hop**?
hops	The frog takes big **hops** in the pond. ■

Ii

isn't	The frog is not in the tank. The frog **isn't** in the tank. ■

Jj

just	I don't have a plane. I **just** have a balloon. ■

Kk

keep   I will **keep** the plane. ■

Ll

let   You can **let** the dog out.

like   I **like** to run with you.

likes   He **likes** to surprise me.

little   The **little** dog is in. ■

looked   He **looked** for the picture.

looks   It **looks** like it will rain.

Mm

makes   The girl **makes** a picture. ■

68

may   You **may** go to the pond.

my   "This is **my** frog," said Meg.

Nn

new   This boat is **new.** ■

Oo

of   She has a box **of** food. ■

oh   "**Oh,** what a big dog!"
he said.

Pp

picture   We can see the **picture.**

playing Todd and Sam are **playing.**

pond The frog likes the **pond.** ■

put Meg **put** Mortimer in the box.

Ss

she The girl looks for a frog.
She can't find a frog. ■

surprise Meg has a **surprise** for us.

Tt

tank The frog is in the **tank.** ■

them This box is for Kim and Rita.
This box is for **them.**

there The boat will stop **there.**

they The boy and girl can run.
They can run.

think   I **think** boats are fun.

Vv

van   We can sit in the **van.** ■

Ww

wanted   I **wanted** to have fun.

wants   She **wants** you to play.

went   They **went** to see the frog.

where   I can't see you.
Where are you? ■

Yy

yet   The van isn't here **yet.**

Word List

The following words are introduced in this book. Each is listed beside the number of the page on which it first appears. The words printed in color are words that students can decode independently, based on elements taught in this program.

The Surprise
(5–9)

5 surprise
 asked
6 frog
 like
7 girls
 boys
8 little

Mortimer Hops!
(10–14)

10 hops
 looks
 don't
11 hop
12 likes
 think
13 can't

Where Is Mortimer?
(15–19)

15 where
 find
 he
16 him
18 looked
 they

They Find Mortimer
(20–27)

20 there
22 went
 them
23 put
 tank
24 new
27 makes
 just

Mortimer Gets Out
(28–33)

28 oh
 isn't
 his
29 of
30 are
 doing
 playing
31 going
32 keep
33 ask

Where Will Mortimer Go?
(34–39)

34 has
 wants

35 home
 may
36 she
 pond
37 let
39 my
 dad
 van

A New Home for Mortimer
(40–44)

40 all
 happy
41 box

The Pond
(45–51)

46 yet
 picture
47 food

The Picture
(54–63)

58 am
 wanted
60 but
61 hat
63 being

K 5
L 6
M 7
N 8